Balance Benders™
Level 3

Series Titles
Balance Benders™
Beginning ▪ Level 1 ▪ Level 2 ▪ Level 3

Written by
Robert Femiano

Graphic Design by
Annette Langenstein ▪ Karla Garrett ▪ Trisha Dreyer

D1088429

© 2010
THE CRITICAL THINKING CO.™
www.CriticalThinking.com
Phone: 800-458-4849 • Fax: 831-393-3277
P.O. Box 1610 • Seaside • CA 93955-1610
ISBN 978-1-60144-228-4

Mixed Sources
Product group from well-managed forests and other controlled sources
www.fsc.org Cert no. SW-COC-002283
© 1996 Forest Stewardship Council
FSC

TABLE OF CONTENTS

The Value of This Book

Move over Sudoku, here come *Balance Benders*™! You can use these books as quick, fun, logic problems or as stepping-stones to success in algebra. Students develop deductive thinking and pre-algebra skills as they solve balance puzzles that are more fun and addictive than Sudoku puzzles! Students must analyze each balance to identify the clues, and then synthesize the information to solve the puzzle. Try one—and then try to stop!

Teaching Suggestions

The solution to each puzzle in this book involves one or more of the algebraic thinking concepts on pages 38-39. After you work through a few puzzles with the student, read and discuss these 10 Balance Tips with the student to make sure he is familiar with all of them. Developing these essential skills used in balancing and solving equations has never been more fun!

A student might occasionally be stumped by a puzzle so an upside-down hint is provided below each puzzle.

It often helps to remind students that the joy of puzzles is being puzzled. Do your best to keep them fun and remember that it is just as important to praise perseverance as it is to praise the correct answer.

About the Author

A longtime puzzle fan, Robert Femiano is a Seattle public school elementary educator and has been for most of his 34-year teaching career. For more than a decade of this time, he was also adjunct faculty at Seattle Pacific University conducting math methods courses. Publications include *Algebraic Problem Solving in the Primary Grades* in the National Council for Teachers of Mathematics peer-reviewed journal and *Quick Thinks Math* books and software by The Critical Thinking Co.™. In 2002, he won the highest honor in education, the Presidential Award for Excellence in Mathematics and Science Teaching.

Which answer can replace the question mark?

a.

b.

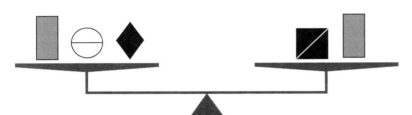

c.

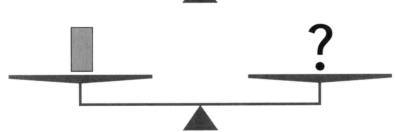

d.

Circle the two answers below that will always be true.

1. ⊖⊖⊖ = ◼   2. ⊖⊖⊖⊖ = ◼

3. ▮▮ = ⊖⊖⊖⊖⊖⊖   4. ◼◆ = ⊖⊖⊖

Hint: On 3rd balance, remove ▮ from both pans.

Which answer can replace the question mark?

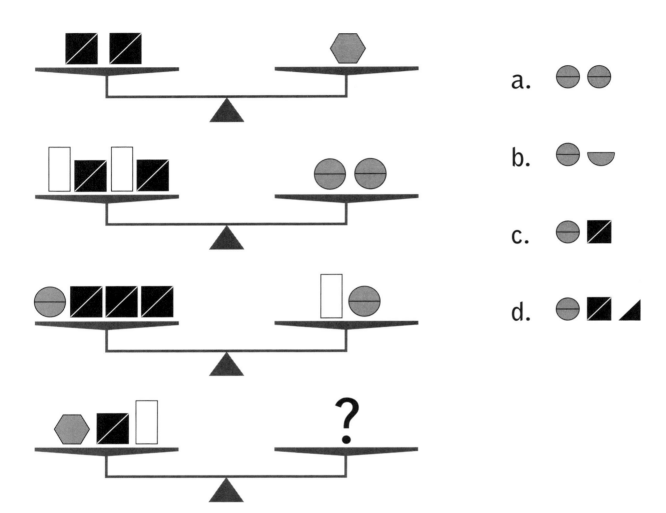

Circle the two answers below that will always be true.

Which answer can replace the question mark?

a. **4**

b. **5**

c. **6**

d. **7**

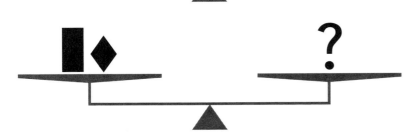

Circle the two answers below that will always be true.

1. ⬤ ☐ = 9

2. ⬤ ☐ = 11

3. ◆ < ▮

4. ◆ > ▮

Hint: From 1st balance, substitute 13 for ◆ ⬤ ☐ on 3rd balance.

Which answer can replace the question mark?

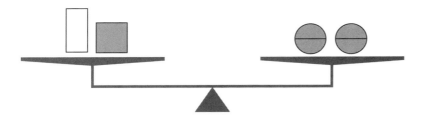

a.

b.

c.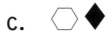

d.

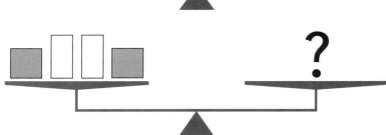

Circle the two answers below that will always be true.

1.

2.

3.

4.

Hint: From 2nd balance, substitute ⬤ for ⬡ on 3rd balance.

Which answer can replace the question mark?

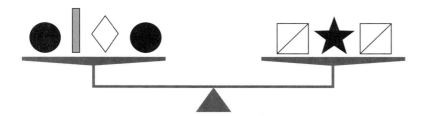

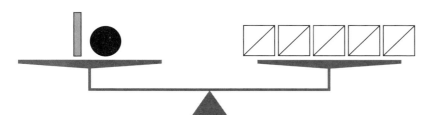　　a.　

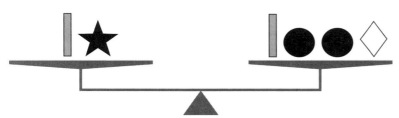　　b.　

c.　

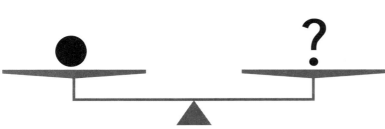　　d.　

Circle the two answers below that will always be true.

1. ⬜⬜ = ▮   2. ⬜⬜⬜ = ▮

3. ⬜⬜⬜ = ★   4. ⬜⬜⬜ = ●

Hint: From 3rd balance, substitute ▮ ● for ★ | ◇ ● | for ● on 1st balance.

Which answer can replace the question mark?

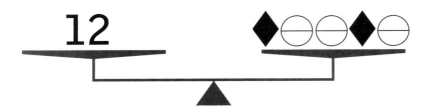

a.

b.

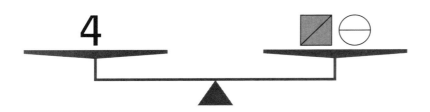

c.

d.

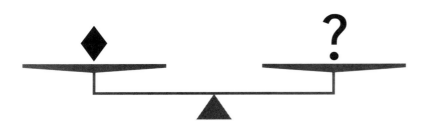

Circle the two answers below that will always be true.

Hint: Triple 2nd balance.

Which answer can replace the question mark?

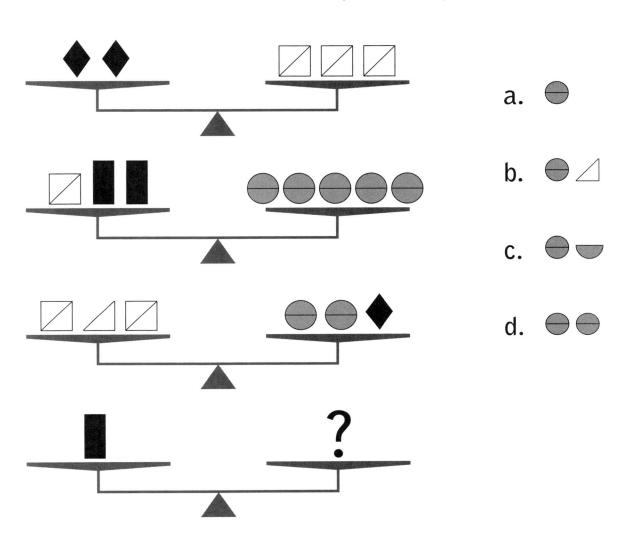

Circle the two answers below that will always be true.

Hint: On 1st balance, divide both pans in half.

Which answer can replace the question mark?

a.

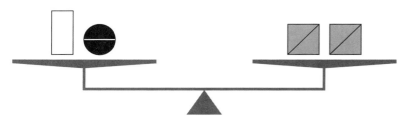

b.

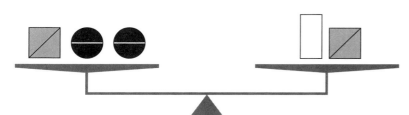

c.

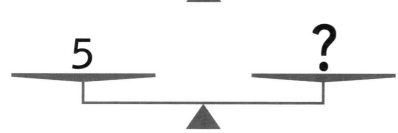

d.

Circle the two answers below that will always be true.

1. □ = ●◢   2. ●● = □

3. ● = 2   4. □ = 2

Hint: On 3rd balance, remove ◢ from both pans.

Which answer can replace the question mark?

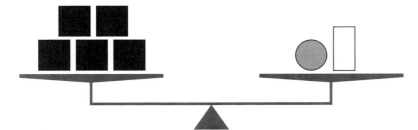

a.

b.

c.

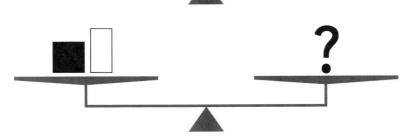

d.

Circle the two answers below that will always be true.

2.

3.

4.

Hint: On 3rd balance, remove ◇ from both pans.

Which answer can replace the question mark?

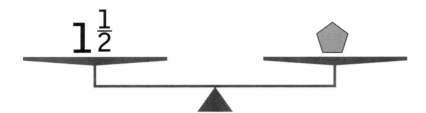

a.

b.

c. ◱◱

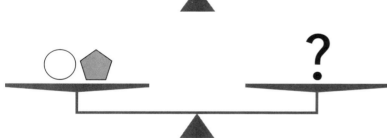

d. ◱◱◿

?

Circle the two answers below that will always be true.

1. ○ = ◆◆   2. ○⬠ = ◱◿

3. ○◆⬠◆ = 4   4. ○⬠ = ◱◱

Hint: Combine 1st and 3rd balances.

Which answer can replace the question mark?

a.

b.

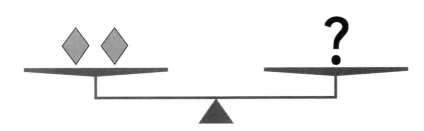

c.

d.

Circle the two answers below that will always be true.

1.    2. $\square \: \hexagon = \diamond \: \diamond$

3. $\hexagon \: \square = \diamond \: \diamond \: \hexagon$ 4. $\diamond = \triangle$

Hint: On 2nd balance, remove ▧ from both pans.

Which answer can replace the question mark?

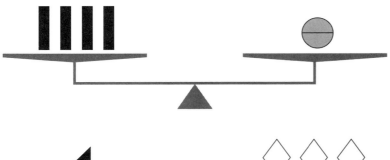

a.

b.

c.

d.

Circle the two answers below that will always be true.

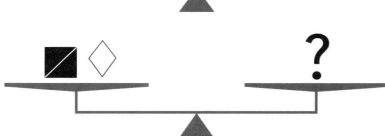

Hint: On 2nd balance, double both pans.

Which answer can replace the question mark?

a.

b.

c.

d.

Circle the two answers below that will always be true.

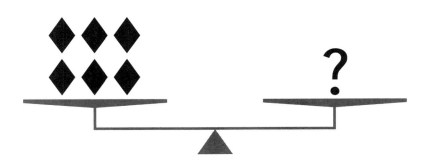

Which answer can replace the question mark?

a.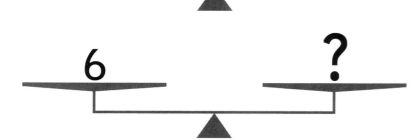

b.

c.

d.

Circle the two answers below that will always be true.

1. ◢ ▽ = $2\frac{1}{2}$ 2. ◯ = $3\frac{1}{2}$

3. ★ = $2\frac{1}{2}$ 4. ◪ = $3\frac{1}{2}$

Hint: Divide 2nd balance in half.

Which answer can replace the question mark?

a.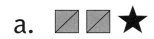

b.

c.

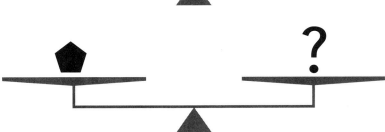

d.

Circle the two answers below that will always be true.

1.

2.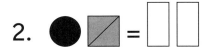

3.

4.

Which answer can replace the question mark?

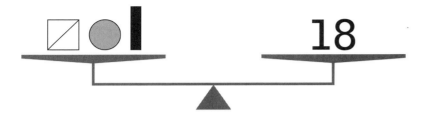

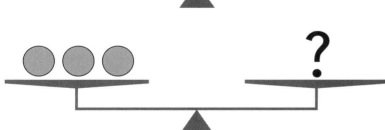

a.

b.

c.

d. IIII △

Circle the two answers below that will always be true.

1. □ + 1 = ▌   2. ▌ + 1 = □

3. □ + 1 = ●   4. ● + 1 = □

Hint: Compare 2nd and 3rd balances.

Which answer can replace the question mark?

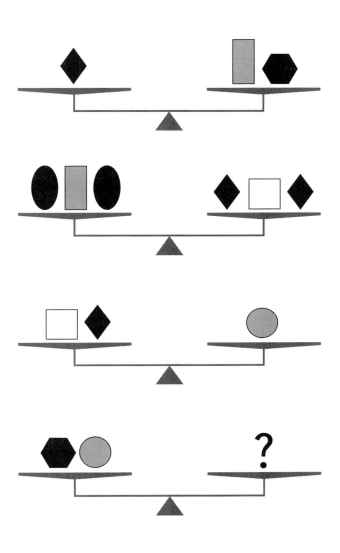

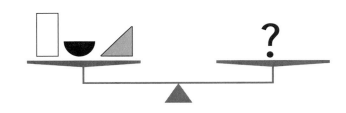

a. 　　　　b. ◆◆

c. ⬤⬤　　　　d. ▮▮

a. ◲◲◲　　b. ◲◲◿

c. ◲⬤　　　d. ◲⬤◲

Balance Benders™

Which answer can replace the question mark?

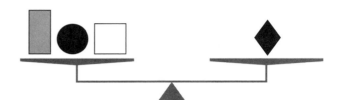

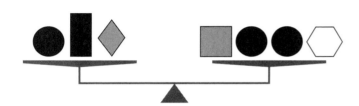

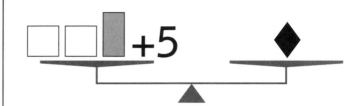

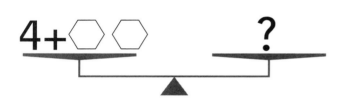

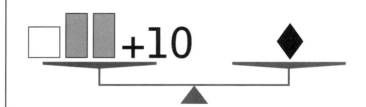

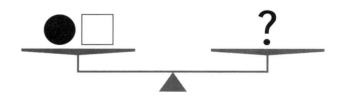

a. ▮▮ (gray)   b. ▮▮ (black)

c. ●●   d. ◆◆

Hint: From 1st balance, substitute 2 + ▮ for ● on 2nd balance.

a. ▮▮ + 15   b. ▮▮▮ + 15

c. ▮▮ + 10   d. ▮▮▮ + 10

Hint: From 2nd balance, substitute □ ▮▮ + 5 for ◆ on 3rd balance.

Which answer can replace the question mark?

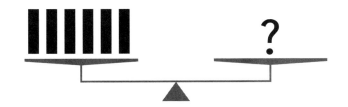

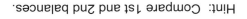

Balance Benders™

Which answer can replace the question mark?

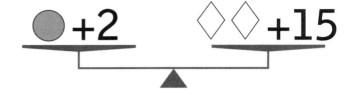

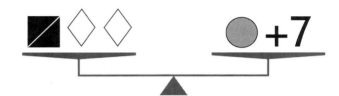

a. ⬤ ⬤ ⬤   b. ⬤ ⬤ ⬛

c. ⬤ ⬛ ⬛   d. ⬛ ⬛ ⬛

a. ◇   b. ◣ ◇

c. ◨ ◇   d. ◨

Hint: On 2nd balance, add ● to both pans.

Hint: On 1st balance, add 5 to both pans.

Which answer can replace the question mark?

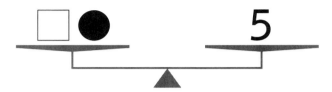

5

6

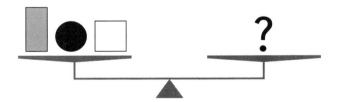

7

?

a. 8   b. 9

c. 10   d. 11

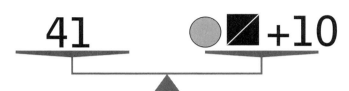

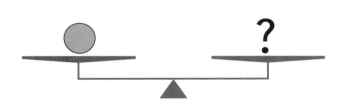

a. 13   b. 17

c. 19   d. 23

Hint: Divide 2nd balance in half.

Hint: Compare 1st and 2nd balances.

Which answer can replace the question mark?

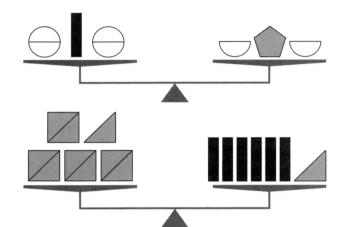

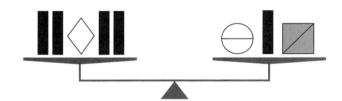

a.    b.

c.    d.

a.    b.

© 2010 The Critical Thinking Co.™ • www.CriticalThinking.com • 800-458-4849

Which answer can replace the question mark?

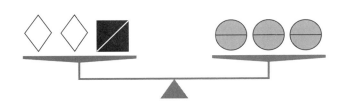

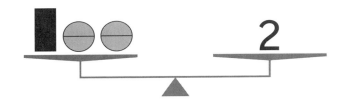

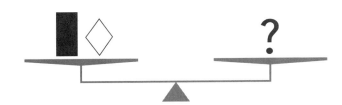

a. ⌣ + 10   b. ⊖ + 10

c. ⊖ ⌣ + 5   d. ⊖ + 5

Hint: On 2nd balance, add 5 to both pans.

a. ⊖ ◪ ⊖   b. ⊖ ⊖ ⌣

c. ⊖ ◨ ◣   d. ⊖ ◨ ◣ ⌣

Hint: Reverse 2nd balance and combine with 1st balance.

Which answer can replace the question mark?

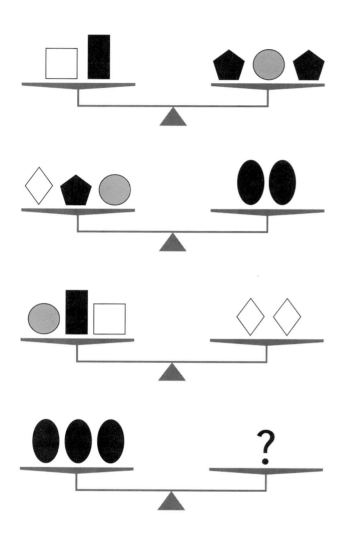

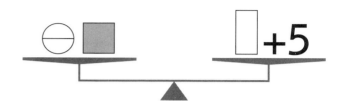

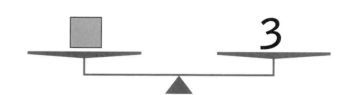

a.  b.

c.  d.

a.   b.

c.  d.

Hint: From 1st balance, substitute ⬟ ● ⬟ for ▮ ☐ on 3rd balance.

Hint: Reverse 2nd balance and combine with 1st balance.

Balance Benders™

Which answer can replace the question mark?

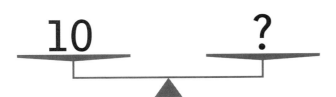

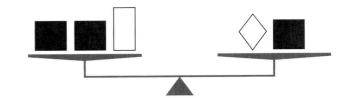

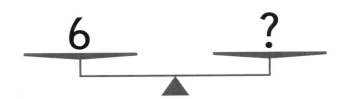

a. ★ ★   b. ★ + 1

c. ★ + 3   d. ★ + 7

a. ⬡   b. ◇

c. ●   d. ▯

 Hint: On 3rd balance, remove ☐ from both pans.

 Hint: On 3rd balance, add ● to each pan.

Which answer can replace the question mark?

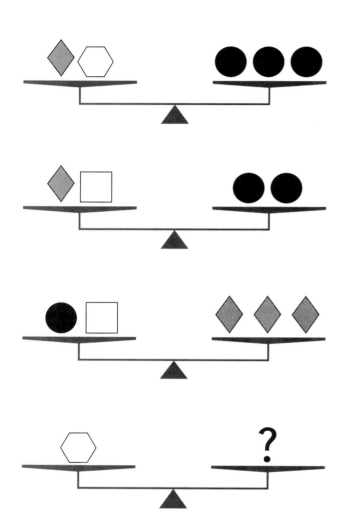

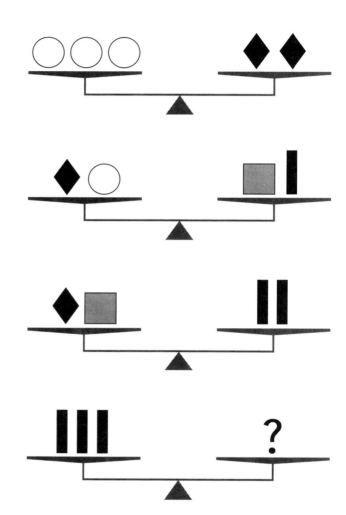

Which answer can replace the question mark?

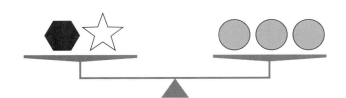

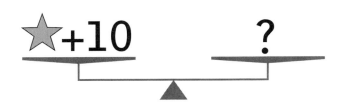

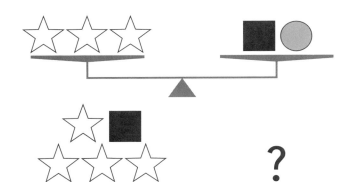

a. ▱

b. ⬤

c. ▱ ◿

d. ⬤ ◗

a.

b.

c.

d.

Balance Benders™

Which answer can replace the question mark?

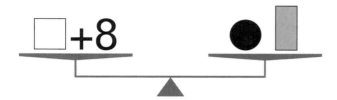

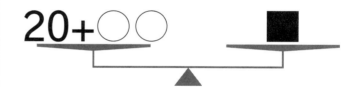

a.

b. ● ● ◇

c. ◇ ◇

d. ▊ ●

a. ■ ○ ○

b. ■ ■ ○

c. ○ ○ ○

d. ■ ■ ○ ○

(c also: ○ ■)

Which answer can replace the question mark?

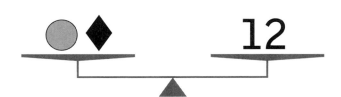

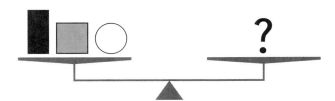

a.    b.    a. 14   b. 15

c. 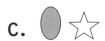   d.   c. 16   d. 17

Hint: From 1st balance, substitute ◇ ▦ ◇ for
▮ ◯ on 2nd balance.

Hint: Compare 2nd and 3rd balances.

Which answer can replace the question mark?

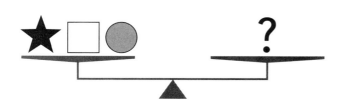

a. 24   b. 26

c. 28   d. 30

a.    b.

c.   d.

Hint: Reverse 3rd balance and combine with 1st balance.

Hint: On 1st balance, add ■ to both pans.

Balance Benders™

Which answer can replace the question mark?

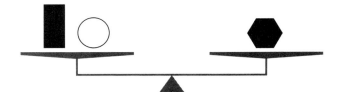

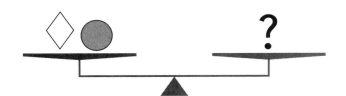

a.    b.

c.    d.

a. ■ ■   b. ■ +2

c. ■ +1   d. ■

Which answer can replace the question mark?

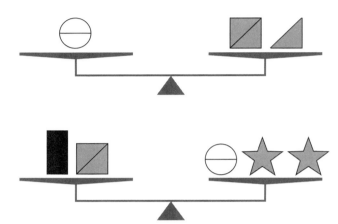

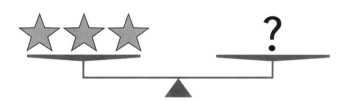

a.

b. ⊖ ⊖

c. ▧ ▧

d. ▮▮ ◿

Hint: Reverse 3rd balance and combine with 1st balance.

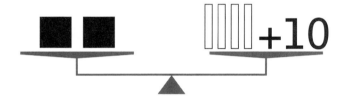

○ +10   ?

a. ▯▯+10   b. ▯▯+15

c. ▯▯+20   d. ▯▯+25

Hint: Divide 2nd balance in half.

Which answer can replace the question mark?

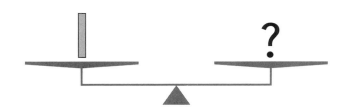

a.

b.

c. ...

a.

b.

c.

d.

Which answer can replace the question mark?

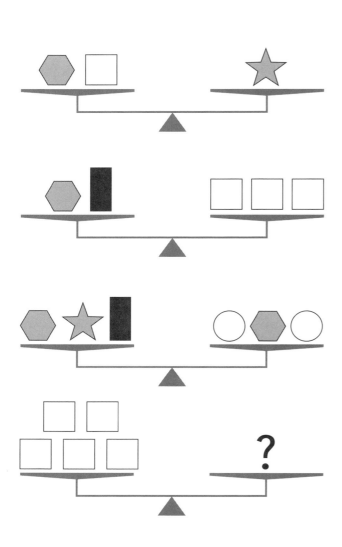

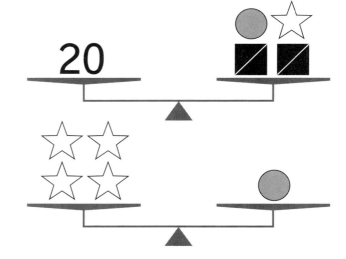

a.  b.

c.  d.

a.   b.

c.  d.

Hint: Reverse 2nd balance and combine with 1st balance.

Hint: Compare 1st and 3rd balances.

Balance Benders™

Which answer can replace the question mark?

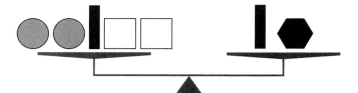

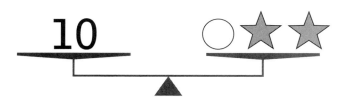

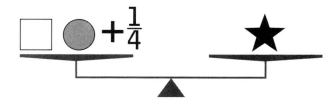

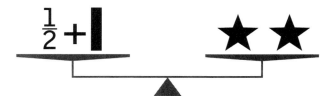

a.    b. ★ ★ ★

a. 14   b. 15

c. ★ ⬤ ▢   d. ⬡ ⬡

c. 16   d. 17

Which answer can replace the question mark?

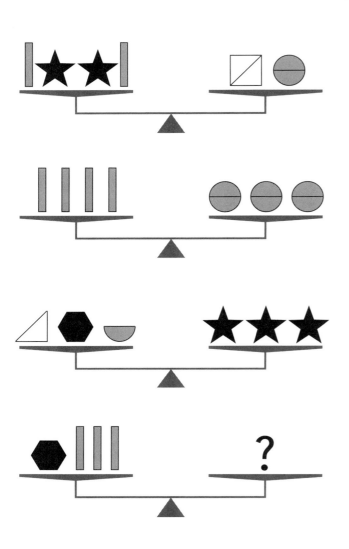

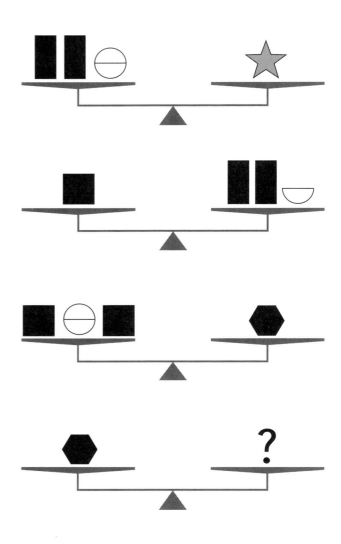

Which answer can replace the question mark?

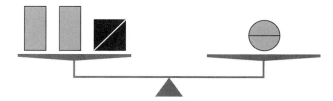

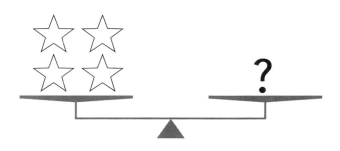

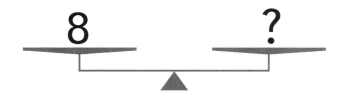

a.   b.

c.   d.

Hint: Divide 1st balance in half.

a. ⬡   b. ▮ ◺

c. ★   d. ▮ ◺

Hint: Reverse 3rd balance and combine with 2nd balance.

BALANCE TIPS
(ALGEBRA CONCEPTS)

1. Reversing the pans does not change the balance of the scale. For example . . .

   If a = b then b = a
   If a > b then b < a

   Symmetric Property of Equality and Inequality

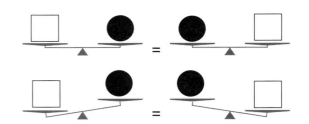

2. Rearranging "weights" does not change the balance of the scale. For example . . .

   a + b = b + a
   If a + b < c then b + a < c
   If a + b > c then b + a > c

   Commutative Property of Equality and Inequality

   a + (b + c) = (a + b) + c

   Associative Property of Equality and Inequality

3. Adding the same "weight" to each pan does not change the balance of the scale. For example . . .

   If a = b then a + c = b + c
   If a < b then a + c < b + c
   If a > b then a + c > b + c

   Addition Property of Equality and Inequality

4. Subtracting the same "weight" from each pan does not change the balance of the scale. For example . . .

   If a = b then a - c = b - c
   If a < b then a - c < b - c
   If a > b then a - c > b - c

   Subtraction Property of Equality and Inequality

5. Multiplying both pans equally (e.g. doubling) does not change the balance of the scale. For example . . .

   If a = b then a * c = b * c
   If a < b then a * c < b * c
   If a > b then a * c > b * c

   Multiplication Property of Equality and Inequality

BALANCE TIPS (Cont.)
(ALGEBRA CONCEPTS)

6. Dividing or partitioning both pans into equally numbered groups (e.g. take half) does not change the balance of the scale. For example . . .

   If a = b then a/c = b/c
   If a < b then a/c < b/c
   If a > b then a/c > b/c

   Division Property of Equality and Inequality

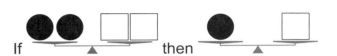

7. Substitute one "weight" for a similar "weight" or group of "weights." For example . . .

   If a = b then "a" can be substituted for "b" in any equation or inequality

   Substitution Property of Equality and Inequality

   If a = b and b = c then a = c
   If a < b and b < c then a < c
   If a > b and b > c then a > c

   Transitive Property of Equality and Inequality

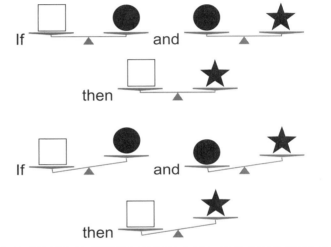

8. Combining two balanced scales does not change the balance of the new scale. For example . . .

   If a = b and c = d then a + c = b + d and a + d = b + c

   Addition and Substitution Properties

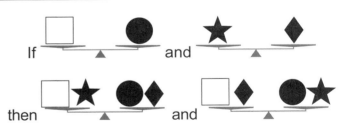

9. Removing a "weight" from one pan of a balanced scale causes an imbalance. For example . . .

   If a + b = c then c > a and c > b

   Equation to Inequality or Trichotomy Property

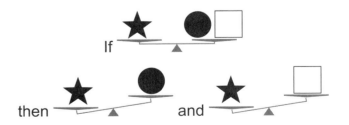

10. When multiplying or dividing, be sure to do the same to all "weights" in the pans. For example . . .

    a * (b + c) = (a * b) + (a * c)

    Distributive Property

Solutions

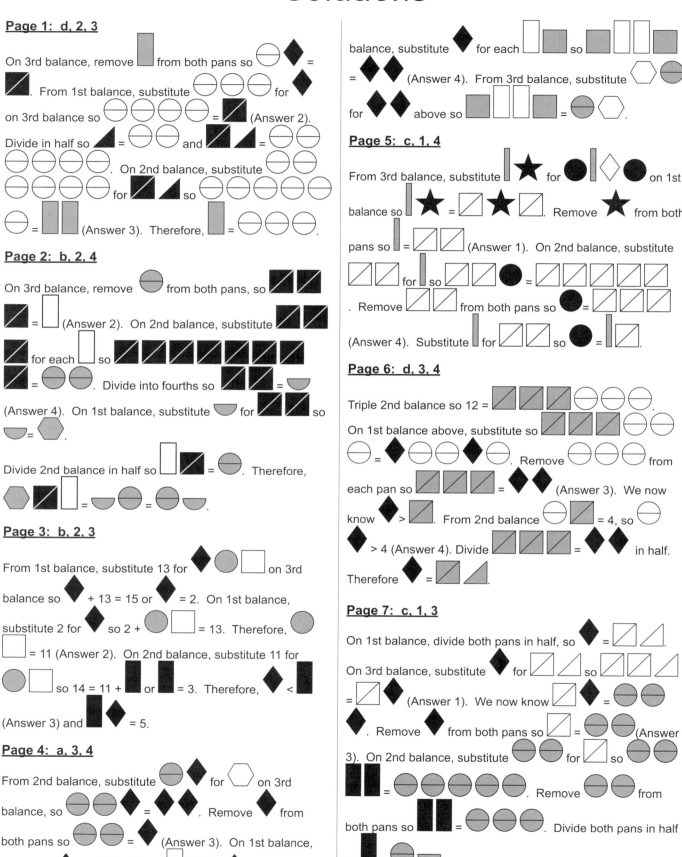

Page 1: d, 2, 3

On 3rd balance, remove ▮ from both pans so ⊖ = ◆ . From 1st balance, substitute ⊖⊖⊖ for ◆ on 3rd balance so ⊖⊖⊖⊖ = ◪ (Answer 2). Divide in half so ◤ = ⊖⊖ and ◺ = ⊖⊖ . On 2nd balance, substitute ⊖⊖⊖ ⊖⊖⊖ for ◤ ◺ so ⊖⊖⊖⊖⊖⊖ ⊖ = ▮▮ (Answer 3). Therefore, ▮ = ⊖⊖⊖ .

Page 2: b, 2, 4

On 3rd balance, remove ⊖ from both pans, so ◹ = ▯ (Answer 2). On 2nd balance, substitute ◹ for each ▯ so ◹◹◹◹◹◹◹◹ ◹ = ◓◓ . Divide into fourths so ◹◹ = ◓ (Answer 4). On 1st balance, substitute ◓ for ◹◹ so ◓ = ⬡ . Divide 2nd balance in half so ▯◹ = ◓ . Therefore, ◓◹▯ = ◓ ◓ .

Page 3: b, 2, 3

From 1st balance, substitute 13 for ◆ ◯ ▢ on 3rd balance so ◆ + 13 = 15 or ◆ = 2. On 1st balance, substitute 2 for ◆ so 2 + ▢ = 13. Therefore, ▢ = 11 (Answer 2). On 2nd balance, substitute 11 for ◯ ▢ so 14 = 11 + ▮ or ▮ = 3. Therefore, ▮ < ◆ (Answer 3) and ▮ ◆ = 5.

Page 4: a, 3, 4

From 2nd balance, substitute ⊖ ◆ for ⬡ on 3rd balance, so ⊖⊖ ◆ = ◆ ◆ . Remove ◆ from both pans so ⊖⊖ = ◆ (Answer 3). On 1st balance, substitute ◆ for ⊖⊖ so ▯▮ = ◆ . On 4th

Page 5: c, 1, 4

balance, substitute ◆ for each ▯ ▮ so ◆◆ = ◆◆ (Answer 4). From 3rd balance, substitute ◆◆ for ⬡ ◓ above so ▮▯▮ = ◓ ⬡ .

From 3rd balance, substitute ▮★ for ● ▯◇● on 1st balance so ▮★ = ▱★▱ . Remove ★ from both pans so ▮ = ▱▱ (Answer 1). On 2nd balance, substitute ▱▱ for ▮ so ▱▱● = ▱▱▱▱ . Remove ▱▱ from both pans so ● = ▱▱▱ (Answer 4). Substitute ▮ for ▱▱ so ●▮ = ▱ .

Page 6: d, 3, 4

Triple 2nd balance so 12 = ◨◨◨⊖⊖⊖ . On 1st balance above, substitute so ⊖ = ◆⊖⊖◆⊖ . Remove ⊖⊖⊖ from each pan so ◨◨◨ = ◆◆ (Answer 3). We now know ◆ > ◨ . From 2nd balance ⊖◨ = 4, so ◆ > 4 (Answer 4). Divide ◨◨◨ = ◆◆ in half. Therefore ◆ = ◨◺ .

Page 7: c, 1, 3

On 1st balance, divide both pans in half, so ◆ = ▱◺ . On 3rd balance, substitute ◆ for ◺◺◺ so ▱▱ = ▱◆ (Answer 1). We now know ◆ ▱◺ = ◓◓ . Remove ◆ from both pans so ▱ = ◓◓ (Answer 3). On 2nd balance, substitute ◓◓ for ▱ so ▮▮ = ◓◓◓◓ . Remove ◓◓ from both pans so ▮▮ = ◓◓ . Divide both pans in half so ▮ = ◓◓ .

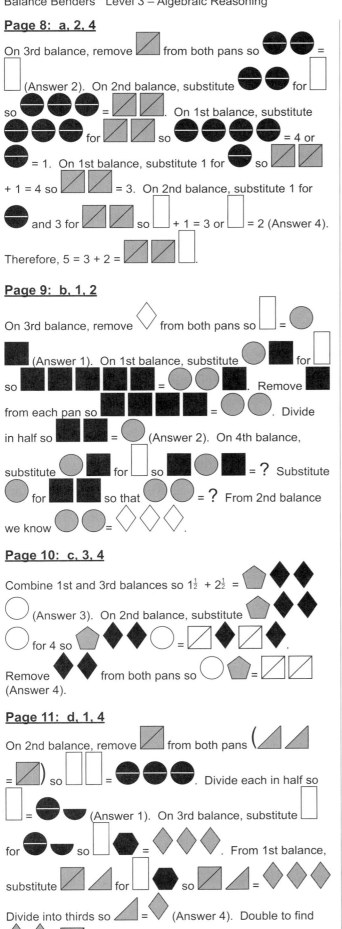

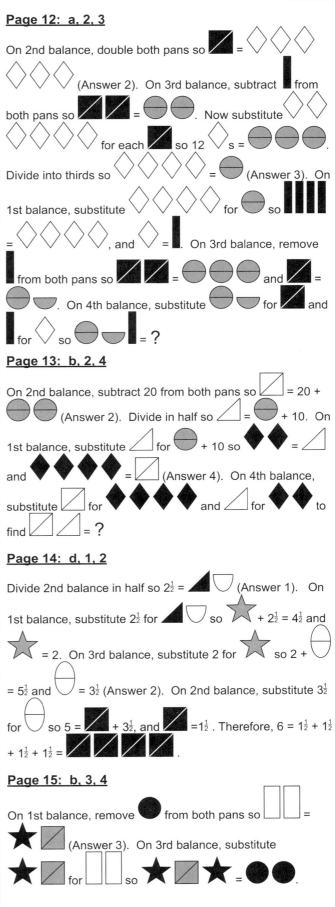

On 2nd balance, substitute 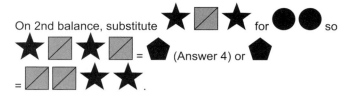 for so

(Answer 4) or .

Page 16: c, 2, 3

Compare 2nd and 3rd balances so 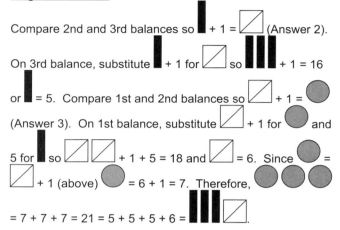 + 1 = (Answer 2).

On 3rd balance, substitute + 1 for so + 1 = 16

or = 5. Compare 1st and 2nd balances so + 1 =

(Answer 3). On 1st balance, substitute + 1 for and

5 for so + 1 + 5 = 18 and = 6. Since

+ 1 (above) = 6 + 1 = 7. Therefore,

= 7 + 7 + 7 = 21 = 5 + 5 + 5 + 6 = .

Page 17 Problem 1: c

From 3rd balance, substitute for on 2nd

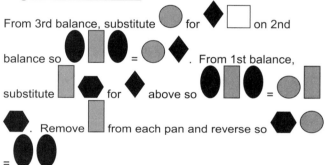

balance so = . From 1st balance,

substitute for above so =

. Remove from each pan and reverse so

= .

Page 17 Problem 2: a

From 2nd balance, substitute for on

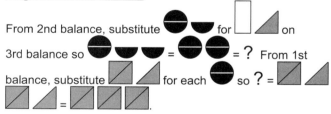

3rd balance so = = ? From 1st

balance, substitute for each so ? =

= .

Page 18 Problem 1: d

On 2nd balance, remove from both pans so =

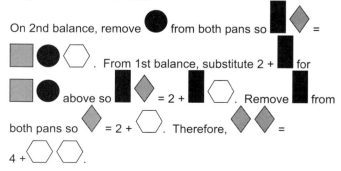

. From 1st balance, substitute 2 + for

above so = 2 + . Remove from

both pans so = 2 + . Therefore, =

4 + .

Page 18 Problem 2: a

From 2nd balance, substitute + 5 for on 3rd

balance so 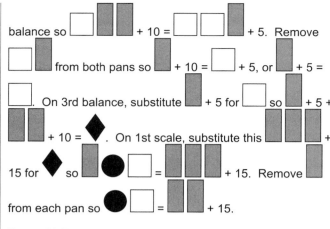 + 10 = + 5. Remove

from both pans so + 10 = + 5, or + 5 =

. On 3rd balance, substitute + 5 for so + 5 +

+ 10 = . On 1st scale, substitute this +

15 for so = + 15. Remove

from each pan so = + 15.

Page 19 Problem 1: d

Compare 1st and 2nd balances so 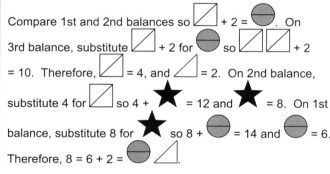 + 2 = . On

3rd balance, substitute + 2 for so + 2

= 10. Therefore, = 4, and = 2. On 2nd balance,

substitute 4 for so 4 + = 12 and = 8. On 1st

balance, substitute 8 for so 8 + = 14 and = 6.

Therefore, 8 = 6 + 2 = .

Page 19 Problem 2: c

On 1st balance, remove from both pans so 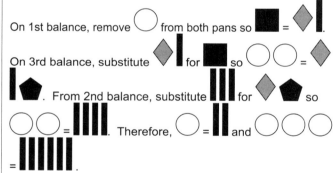 = .

On 3rd balance, substitute for so = .

From 2nd balance, substitute for so

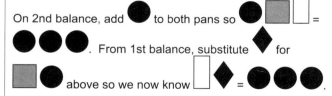

= . Therefore, = and

= .

Page 20 Problem 1: a

On 2nd balance, add to both pans so 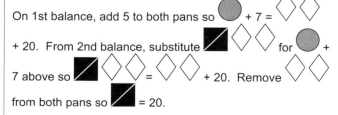 =

. From 1st balance, substitute for

above so we now know = .

Page 20 Problem 2: d

On 1st balance, add 5 to both pans so + 7 =

+ 20. From 2nd balance, substitute for +

7 above so = + 20. Remove

from both pans so = 20.

Page 21 Problem 1: b

Compare 1st and 2nd balances so ● + 1 = ▮. On 3rd balance, substitute ● + 1 for ▮ so ● ● + 1 = 7, and ● = 3. On 1st balance, substitute 3 for ● so ☐ + 3 = 5 and ☐ = 2. Substitute 2 for ☐ on 2nd balance so 2 + ▮ = 6 and ▮ = 4. Therefore, ● ☐ = 4 + 3 + 2 = 9.

Page 21 Problem 2: b

Divide 2nd balance in half so ◣ = 10 = ⬤. On 1st balance, substitute ◣ + 10 for ⬤ so 41 = ◣ + 10 + ◩ + 10. From both pans, remove 20 so 21 = ◣ ◩. Divide into thirds so ◣ = 7 and ◩ = 14. On 2nd balance, substitute 14 for ◩ so 14 + 20 = 34 = ⬤ ⬤. Therefore, 17 = ⬤.

Page 22 Problem 1: a

From 1st balance, substitute ◇ + 6 for ▮▮ on 2nd balance so ⬤ ◇ + 6 = 20 and ⬤ ◇ = 14. On 3rd balance, substitute 14 for ⬤ ◇ so 14 + ⬡ = 22. Therefore, ⬡ = 8 and 16 = ⬡ ⬡.

Page 22 Problem 2: d

On 2nd balance, remove ◺ from both pans and divide in half so ◩ ◩ ◩ ◩ = ▮▮▮▮▮▮ and ◩ ◩ = ▮▮▮. On 3rd balance, substitute ◩ ◩ for ▮▮▮ so ◩ ◩ ◇ = ⬭ ◩ ◩. From both pans, remove ◩ ◩ so ◇ = ⬭. On 1st balance, remove ⬭ from both pans (⬭ ⬭ = ⬭) so ◩ ▮ = ⬠. Substitute ◩ ◇ from above for ⬭ so ◩ ◇ ▮ = ⬠.

Page 23 Problem 1: b

On 2nd balance, add 5 to both pans so ◆ + 10 = ⬭ ⬭ + 5. On 1st balance, substitute ⬭ ⬭ + 5 for ◆ + 10 so ▮ ⬭ ⬭ = ⬭ ⬭ + 5. From both pans, remove ⬭ so ▮ = ⬭ + 5. Therefore, ▮ ▮ = ⬭ + 10.

Page 23 Problem 2: d

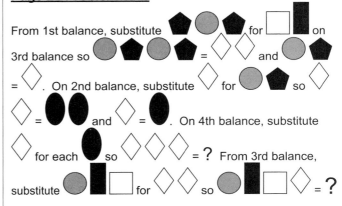

Reverse 2nd balance and combine with 1st balance so ◇ ◪ + 1 = ⬤ ⬤ ⬤ ⬤ ◪. From both pans, remove ◪ so ◇ ◇ + 1 = ⬤ ⬤ ⬤. Divide in half so ◇ + ½ = ⬤ ⬤. On 3rd balance, substitute ◇ + ½ for ⬤ ⬤ so ▮ ◇ + ½ = 2 or ▮ ◇ = 1½. From 2nd balance, we know ◖ ◣ = ½. Therefore, 1 + ½ = ◖ ◪ ◖ ◣ ▮ = ◇.

Page 24 Problem 1: b

From 1st balance, substitute ⬟ ⬤ ⬟ for ☐ ▮ on 3rd balance so ⬤ ⬟ ⬤ ⬟ = ◇ ◇ and ▮ = ◇. On 2nd balance, substitute ◇ for ▮ so ◇ = ⬤ ⬟ so ◇ = ⬬ ⬬ and ◇ = ⬬. On 4th balance, substitute ◇ for each ⬬ so ◇ ◇ ◇ = ? From 3rd balance, substitute ⬤ ▮ ☐ for ◇ ◇ ◇ so ⬤ ▮ ☐ ◇ = ?

Page 24 Problem 2: b

Reverse 2nd balance and combine with 1st balance so ▮ ⬡ ☐ = ▮ ▮ + 5. Remove ▮ from both pans so ⬭ ⬡ = ▮ + 5. From 3rd balance, substitute 3 for ▮ so ⬭ ⬡ = 3 + 5 = 8.

Page 25 Problem 1: c

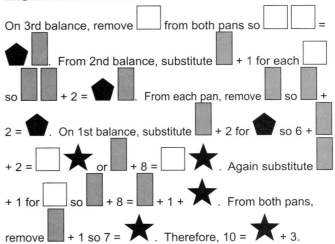

On 3rd balance, remove ☐ from both pans so ☐ ☐ = ⬟. From 2nd balance, substitute ▮ + 1 for each ☐ so ▮ + 2 = ⬟. From each pan, remove ▮ so ▮ + 2 = ⬟. On 1st balance, substitute ▮ + 2 for ⬟ so 6 + ▮ + 2 = ☐ ★ or ▮ + 8 = ☐ ★. Again substitute ▮ + 1 for ☐ so ▮ + 8 = ▮ + 1 + ★. From both pans, remove ▮ + 1 so 7 = ★. Therefore, 10 = ★ + 3.

Page 25 Problem 2: a

On 3rd balance, add ⬤ to each pan so 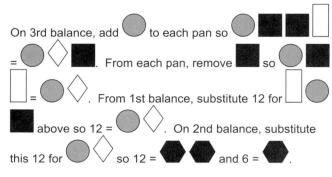 = ▭◇■. From each pan, remove ■ so

▭ = ⬤◇. From 1st balance, substitute 12 for

■ above so 12 = ⬤◇. On 2nd balance, substitute

this 12 for ⬤◇ so 12 = ⬡⬡ and 6 = ⬡.

Page 26 Problem 1: d

Combine 1st and 3rd balances so ◆⬡⬤▭ = ⬤

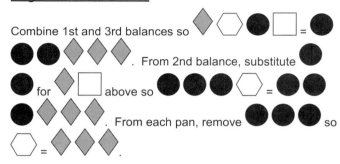. From 2nd balance, substitute

⬤ for ▭ above so ⬤⬤⬤⬡ = ⬤⬤

⬤◆◆◆. From each pan, remove ⬤⬤⬤ so

⬡ = ◆◆◆.

Page 26 Problem 2: c

Combine 2nd and 3rd balanes so ◆◆◯▮ = ▮▮

▮▮. From 1st balance, substitute ◯◯◯ for ◆◆

above so ◯◯◯◯ = ▮▮▮▮▮. From both

pans, remove ▮ so ◯◯◯◯ = ▮▮▮.

Page 27 Problem 1: a

On 1st balance, add ◻ to each pan so 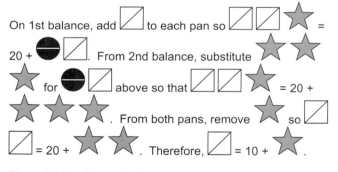 =

20 + ◻. From 2nd balance, substitute

⊖ for ◻ above so that ◻◻ = 20 +

⭐⭐⭐. From both pans, remove ⭐ so ◻

◻ = 20 + ⭐⭐. Therefore, ◻ = 10 + ⭐.

Page 27 Problem 2: b

Combine 1st and 3rd balances, so 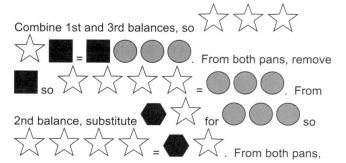. From both pans, remove

▮ so ☆☆☆☆ = ◯◯◯. From

2nd balance, substitute ⬡ for ◯◯◯ so

☆☆☆☆ = ⬡. From both pans,

Page 28 Problem 1: c

remove ☆ so ☆☆☆ = ⬡. On 4th balance,

substitute ⬡ for ☆☆☆ so 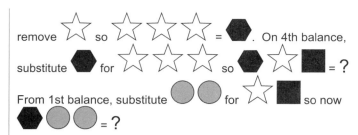 = ?

From 1st balance, substitute ◯◯ for ☆■ so now

⬡◯◯ = ?

Page 28 Problem 1: c

On 1st balance, add ⬤ to both pans so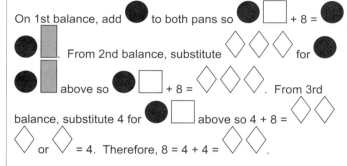

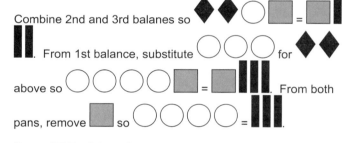. From 2nd balance, substitute ◇◇◇ for

▮ above so ⬤◻ + 8 = ◇◇◇. From 3rd

balance, substitute 4 for ⬤◻ above so 4 + 8 = ◇◇

◇ or ◇ = 4. Therefore, 8 = 4 + 4 = ◇◇.

Page 28 Problem 2: b

On 3rd balance, add 20 to both pans so 40 + ◯◯ =

▮ + 20. On 1st balance, substitute 40 + ◯◯ for 20 +

▮ so ◇ = 40 + ◯◯. From 2nd balance, substitute

◯◯◯ for ◇ so ◯◯◯ = 40 + ◯◯.

Therefore, ◯ = 40. On 2nd balance, substitute 40 for each

◯ so 40 + 40 + 40 = ◇ = 120. On 1st balance, substitute

120 for ◇ so 120 = 20 + ▮ and ▮ = 100. ◇◇ =

120 + 120 = 240 = ? Therefore, 240 = 100 + 100 + 40 =

▮▮◯.

Page 29 Problem 1: c

From 1st balance, substitute ◇▮◇ for ◯▮ on 2nd

balance so ▮◇▮◇ = ⬭⬭. Divide in half so

▮◇⬭ = ⬭. On 3rd balance, substitute ⬭ for ◇

so ⬭⬭ = ☆☆ or ⬭ = ☆. From 2nd balance,

substitute ⬭⬭ for ▮◇◯ on 4th balance so ⬭⬭

= ? Substitute ☆ for ⬭ so ⬭☆ = ?

Page 29 Problem 2: d

Compare 2nd and 3rd balances so 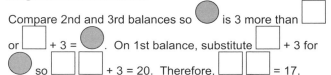 is 3 more than ☐ or ☐ + 3 = ◯. On 1st balance, substitute ☐ + 3 for ◯ so ☐ ☐ + 3 = 20. Therefore, ☐ ☐ = 17.

Page 30 Problem 1: a

Reverse 3rd balance and combine with 1st balance so

20 + 12 = ☐ ★ ◯ ◯. From 2nd balance,

substitute ◯ ◯ for ☐ ★ so 20 + 12 = 32 =

◯ ◯ ◯ ◯. Divide into fourths to find ◯ = 8. On

2nd balance, substitute 8 for each ◯ so 8 + 8 = ☐ ★.

On 4th balance, substitute 16 for ☐ ★ and 8 for ◯

so 16 + 8 = **?** = 24.

Page 30 Problem 2: c

On 1st balance, add ■ to both pans so ■ ★ + 10

= ■ ■ ■. From 2nd balance, substitute 30 for

■ ★ so 30 + 10 = ■ ■ ■ ■ or 10 = ■.

On 3rd balance, substitute 10 for ■ so 10 + ☐ = 25, so

☐ = 15. On 2nd balance, substitute 10 for ■ so 10 +

★ = 30 so ★ = 20. Therefore, ☐ ☐ = 15 + 15 = 30

= 20 + 10 = ★ + 10.

Page 31 Problem 1: c

Reverse 3rd balance and combine with 1st balance so ☐

■ ◯ = ☐ ☆ ☆ ☆. From both pans, remove

■ so ◯ = ☆ ☆ ☆. On 2nd balance,

substitute ☆ ☆ ☆ for ■ ◯ from above so now

☆ ☆ ☆ = ⬡. From 3rd balance, substitute

■ for ☆ ☆ above so ☆ ■ ■ = ⬡.

Page 31 Problem 2: d

From 2nd balance, substitute ◯ + 4 for ◇ on 1st balance

so ■ + 2 = ◯ + 4 + 3 or ■ = ◯ + 5. On 3rd

balance, substitute ◯ + 5 for ■ so ◯ ◯ + 5 = 7 so

◯ = 1. On 3rd balance, substitute 1 for ◯ so 1 + ■ =

7 so ■ = 6. On 1st balance, substitute 6 for ■ so 6 + 2

= ◇ + 3 so ◇ = 5. Therefore, ◇ ◯ = 5 + 1 = 6 = ■.

Page 32 Problem 1: a

Reverse 3rd balance and combine with 1st balance so ⊖

⊖ ◺ = ■ ◸ ◺. From 2nd balance, substitute ⊖

★ ★ for ■ so ⊖ ⊖ ◺ = ⊖ ★. From each pan, remove ⊖

★ ★ ◺ and ⌣ = ★. Therefore,

= ⊖ ⌣.

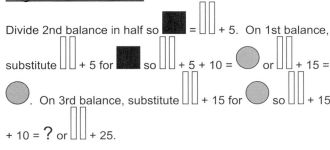

Page 32 Problem 2: d

Divide 2nd balance in half so ■ = ‖ + 5. On 1st balance,

substitute ‖ + 5 for ■ so ‖ + 5 + 10 = ◯ or ‖ + 15 =

◯. On 3rd balance, substitute ‖ + 15 for ◯ so ‖ + 15

+ 10 = **?** or ‖ + 25.

Page 33 Problem 1: b

Reverse 2nd balance and combine with 1st balance so ◹

■ ■ ■ ■ = ◹ ☆ ⊖. From both pans, remove

◹ so ■ ■ ■ = ☆ ⊖. From 3rd balance,

substitute ☆ ☆ ☆ for ⊖ above so that ■ ■

■ = ☆ ☆ ☆ ☆ or ■ = ☆. On 2nd

balance, substitute ■ for ☆ so ◹ ■ = ■ ■ ■.

From both pans, remove ■ so ◹ = ■ ■.

Page 33 Problem 2: d

Divide 2nd balance in half so ◹ + 10 = ◯. On 1st

balance, substitute ◹ + 10 for ◯ so ◹ ◹ + 10 =

★ | + 10. From 3rd balance, substitute ★ ★ for

each ◹ above so ★ ★ ★ ★ + 10 = ★

| + 10. From both pans, remove ★ + 10 so ★ ★ ★

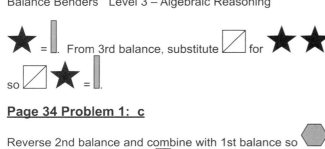 = . From 3rd balance, substitute ▱ for ★★

so ▱★ = ▮.

Page 34 Problem 1: c

Reverse 2nd balance and combine with 1st balance so

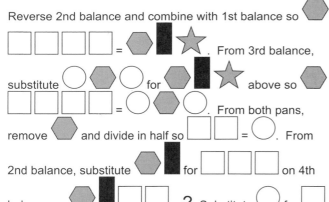

From 3rd balance, substitute ○⬡○ for ⬡ above so ... From both pans, remove ⬡ and divide in half so □□ = ○. From 2nd balance, substitute ⬡ for □□□ on 4th balance so ⬡▮□□ = ? Substitute ○ for □ from above so ⬡▮○ = ?

Page 34 Problem 2: b

Compare 1st and 3rd balances so ◪ = 5. On 3rd balance, substitute 5 for ◪ so 5 + ○☆ = 15 and ○☆ = 10. From 2nd balance, substitute ☆☆☆☆☆ for ○ above so ☆☆☆☆☆☆ = 10 or ☆ = 2. Therefore, 12 = 10 + 2 = ○☆☆.

Page 35 Problem 1: d

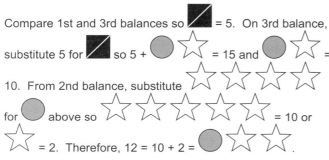

Double 1st balance so □□○○ + ½ = ★★. On 3rd balance, substitute ★★ for ★★ so ½ + ▮ = □□○○ + ½ or ▮ = □□○○. On 2nd balance, remove ▮ from each pan so ○○□□ = ⬢. Substitute ▮ for ○○□□ from above. Therefore, ▮ = ⬢ and ▮▮ = ⬢⬢.

Page 35 Problem 2: b

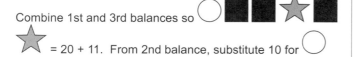

Combine 1st and 3rd balances so ○■■★ = 20 + 11. ★ = 20 + 11. From 2nd balance, substitute 10 for ○

above so ■■■ + 10 = 20 + 11 or ■■■ = 21, and ■ = 7. On 1st balance, substitute 7 for each ■ so ○ + 7 + 7 = 20, and ○ = 6. On 2nd balance, substitute 6 for ○ so 10 = 6 + ★★ and ★ = 2. Therefore, ○■★ = 6 + 7 + 2 = 15.

Page 36 Problem 1: a

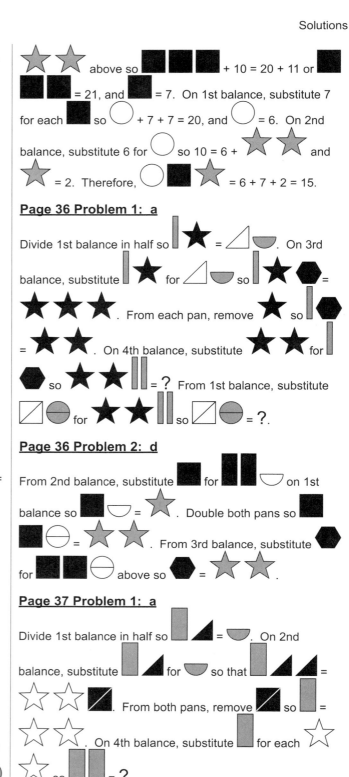

Divide 1st balance in half so ▮★ = △◗. On 3rd balance, substitute ▮★ for △◗ so ▮★⬡ = ★★★. From each pan, remove ★ so ▮⬡ = ★★. On 4th balance, substitute ★★ for ▮ so ⬢★★▮▮ = ? From 1st balance, substitute ▱◑ for ★★▮▮ so ▱◑ = ?.

Page 36 Problem 2: d

From 2nd balance, substitute ■ for ▮▮◡ on 1st balance so ■◡ = ★. Double both pans so ■◓ = ★★. From 3rd balance, substitute ■■◡ for above so ⬢ = ★★.

Page 37 Problem 1: a

Divide 1st balance in half so ▮◣ = ◡. On 2nd balance, substitute ▮◣ for ◡ so that ▮◣◣ = ☆☆◪. From both pans, remove ◪ so ☆☆ = ▮. On 4th balance, substitute ▮ for each ☆ so ☆ ▮▮ = ?

Page 37 Problem 2: c

Reverse 3rd balance and combine with 2nd balance so ⬡ ▮▮ = ●▱ + 8. On 1st balance, substitute this ▱ + 8 for ⬡ ▮▮ so ●▱★ = ●▱ + 8. From each pan, remove ●▱ so ★ = 8.